W9-DJM-812

the Pet Set ®

by
Doug & Jean

"Dan, your alarm is barking."

Distributed in the U.S.A. by T.F.H. Publications, Inc., 211 West Sylvania Avenue, P.O. Box 27, Neptune City, N.J. 07753; in England by T.F.H. (Gt. Britain) Ltd., 13 Nutley Lane, Reigate, Surrey; in Canada to the book store and library trade by Clarke, Irwin & Company, Clarwin House, 791 St. Clair Avenue West, Toronto 10, Ontario; in Canada to the pet trade by Rolf C. Hagen Ltd., 3225 Sartelon Street, Montreal 382, Quebec; in Southeast Asia by Y.W. Ong, 9 Lorong 36 Geylang, Singapore 14; in Australia and the south Pacific by Pet Imports Pty. Ltd., P.O. Box 149, Brookvale 2100, N.S.W., Australia. Published by T.F.H. Publications Inc. Ltd., The British Crown Colony of Hong Kong.

The PET SET

"He keeps bringing this little girl
home from school."

Copyright ©1972, 1973, 1974, 1975, 1976, 1977 by Doug & Jean Borgstedt

The PET SET

"You can see he missed us terribly!"

The PET SET

"No I <u>don't</u> think we should wait
till we get off the turnpike!"

The PET SET

"Looks like Edna's boyfriend got away again."

The PET SET

"It's worth a try."

The PET SET

© D&J Borgstedt 1973

Doug & Jean

3-6

"Harry's not as fond of them as I am."

The PET SET

"I don't think it makes me look distinguished --
I think it makes me look nutty."

The PET SET

© D&J Borgstedt

"Flea collars--for four."

The PET SET

"Mine's two years old, too."

The PET SET

"She has this nasty habit of catching mice."

The PET SET

"Brace yourself--he's fetched all
the neighbors' papers again!"

The PET SET

"Don't worry, Mr. Sylvester--Champ <u>likes</u> people who smell like a dog."

The PET SET

"Goodnight, dear."

The PET SET

"You're right--they DO have wall-to-wall cats!"

The PET SET

"Don't worry Champ--she's only like
this when you're sheddin'."

The PET SET

"No we're NOT the party who ordered
50 lbs. of kittee litter!"

The PET SET

"Congratulations! It's six boys and two girls!"

The PET SET

"He has a great sense of humor, Doc--plays dead every time he hears your name!"

The PET SET

"She's just crazy about those new double-knits!"

The PET SET

"He hates water. Can you dry clean him?"

The PET SET

"It's the car pool for obedience school."

The PET SET

"On the other hand, they say little dogs are, uh--smarter."

The PET SET

"That's funny--Puss usually jumps up on the bed when you let her in."

The PET SET

"Don't kid yourself--they're for real!"

The PET SET

"He always picks our tree."

The PET SET

"One nice thing about planting--
when it's done, it's <u>done!</u>"

The PET SET

"Smart cat! Warmest spot in the house and she can't see the commercials!"

The PET SET

"Relax, Betsy--no burglar could get by Mopsy!"

The PET SET

"After dinner you can all take turns holding him."

The PET SET

"We better beat it before they find out
whose dog it is!"

The PET SET

"Champ's intentions are good--it's just his judgment that's bad."

The PET SET

"They certainly ARE dependents!"

The PET SET

"No thanks--somebody gave him a pair last Easter!"

The PET SET

XMAS GIFTS RETURNED HERE

12-26

Doug & Jean

© D&J Borgstedt

"For one mad moment I thought of keeping it."

The PET SET

"I'll bet if you took them to the office
they'd go like hotcakes!"

The PET SET

"Sure they're smart--but they're not THAT smart."

The PET SET

"It is not! It's their pet monkey."

The PET SET

"One of us forgot to turn off the water last night!"

The PET SET

"MUST you run around collecting doggy bags
from other tables?"

The PET SET

"I want two hamsters and a baby brother."

The PET SET

"Get Calico to carry in her toy mouse--
that broke it up last year."

The PET SET

"It's getting harder and harder
to get through to him."

The PET SET

"Be ready to run if they find out he's ours!"

The PET SET

"Peaceful isn't it? They're not on speaking terms."

The PET SET

"Kinda dresses up the place, don't ya think?"

© D&J Borgstedt

1-23

The PET SET

"Isn't it thrilling to see them fly free!"

The PET SET

"No, no--THAT one over there. Oops, you missed him! Here he comes--there he goes--"

The PET SET

"Marvin's so proud--he finally taught him to pray."

The PET SET

"City dog--it boggles his mind."

The PET SET

"Wag harder, Rags!"

The PET SET

"Sled dogs. Can't stand a warm house."

The PET SET

"Try to think of it as romance."

The PET SET

"Whatever you may think of it, Sylvia--the sports section is NOT for the birds!"

The PET SET

"Now if you'd like one that's a <u>real</u> individualist--"

The PET SET

"I'm glad we persuaded those folks upstairs to get rid of that noisy puppy."

The PET SET

"She can spot one every time!"

The PET SET

"Any faithful employee who DOESN'T want one of the wife's kittens?"

The PET SET

"Well, for starters--"

The PET SET

"I'd **LOVE** to give you one--if I could only decide which one to part with."

The PET SET

"Pick out anything you want, darling."

The PET SET

"Doesn't take them long to figure
who's the soft touch."

The PET SET

"I hope he'll eat it--it's my report card."

The PET SET

"It's one of our most popular designs."

The PET SET

"--and you get your choice of a doggy bag or a kitty bag."

The PET SET

"Somehow, I thought that when we got a station wagon, it would be different."

The PET SET

"For Pete's sake--not the waterbed!"

The PET SET

"That's great--hold it!"

The PET SET

"I hope <u>you</u> don't hear what I think <u>I</u> hear!"

The PET SET

12-2 © D & J Borgstedt

Doug & Jean

"It has silver fins and six black dots."

The PET SET

"It's YOUR turn to hold him, Sylvia.."

The PET SET

"Sure is a cozy way to beat the fuel shortage."

The PET SET

"I know! Weigh each end and add them together."

The PET SET

"Now if you REALLY want something to make your place burglar-proof..."

The PET SET

"Now I'll show you how I call him off--"

The PET SET

"We never should have let him taste hamburger."

The PET SET

"Put them right back in their cage! You KNOW
they make your Mother nervous!"

The PET SET

"He's okay Mom--it's just the vet bill."

The PET SET

c D&J Borgstedt

5-1

Doug & Jean

"Just between us, I have the same problem."

The PET SET

© D&J Borgstedt

Doug & Jean   11-3

"Praise him, dear--he's learning
to fetch the paper."

The PET SET

"And the B's are Billy, Bonnie, Betty, Bob,--"

The PET SET

"New brood of guppies..."

The PET SET

"All right, now let's see if he'll follow
you back to school."

The PET SET

"I hope we can get our money back
on those dog beds."

The PET SET

"Hurry, Roger!"

The PET SET

"You know very well we're <u>not</u> out here to play!"

The PET SET

"We want one to cheer us up after
the 6 o'clock news."

The PET SET

"If they're such good swimmers,
how come she won't let go?"

The PET SET

"Now what seems to be the problem?"

The PET SET

6-13

"How about I take her vitamins--
give her my sedative."

The PET SET

6-8

"The vet said it's easy...just rub his throat
and he'll swallow them:"

The PET SET

8-3

"If you don't tie him up, the score's
going to be love nothing!"

The PET SET

"It says: Happy Birthday!--from
your uncle in Australia."

The PET SET

"If he calls 'em sardines once more
I'm gonna let him have it!"

The PET SET

"Okay, you win--we'll get a king-size bed."

The PET SET

"That's $5 for the kitten and $27.50 for the dish, collar, brush, ball--"

The PET SET

"Now try the <u>first</u> flavor again--"

The PET SET

"Of course the car keys aren't lost--I put them
right here just a minute ago!"

The PET SET

5-7

"G'wan, Butch--fetch it!"

The PET SET

© D&J Borgstedt

"My wife doesn't understand us, Doc."

The PET SET

"Monday 12, Tuesday 20, today 30--
d'ya spose it's MAGIC?"

The PET SET

"--and bless those less fortunate
who have no turkey--"

The PET SET

"Even among intellectuals, you can occasionally detect signs of insecurity."

The PET SET

"She hasn't got any husband
--she makes 'em herself."

The PET SET

"Guess what I brought for my Valentine!"

The PET SET

"So many dognappings lately, we got a bodyguard for Tiger."

The PET SET

"You keep that monster away from my Fifi!"

The PET SET

"YOU explain to him about waiting till half-time!"

The PET SET

"Please--DO go ahead of us!"

The PET SET

"I THINK they're singing 'Silent Night'."

The PET SET

"Oh dear! DOG people!"

The PET SET

"Dan, <u>your</u> cat wants in."

The PET SET

5-25

Doug & Jean

© D&J Borgstedt

"It may be 'speaking' to you, but
it's plain old barking to me."

The PET SET

"I put him in your closet where
he couldn't reach things."

The PET SET

"It may be a jaunt to you, but it's a pain
in the feet to me!"

The PET SET

"Any luck, dear?"

The PET SET

"Gee Dad, I wish they were that glad to see me!"

The PET SET

"MY day? Just average."

The PET SET

"You'd never guess they raise African love birds."

The PET SET

"MOM! Johnny drank my guppies!"

The PET SET

"Well, at least only <u>one</u> of them is shedding!"

The PET SET

"We hoped you'd have something
in platform soles."

The PET SET

"Hi, Butch!"

The PET SET

"How can you bear not to leave a FEW scraps?"

The PET SET

"It's all written down there: his playtime's at 7; dinner at 8; walk at 9; bedtime at 10."

The PET SET

"You'll be sorry when you've nobody to walk the dog, put out the cat, feed the fish, cover the bird-"

The PET SET

"First the good news--Calico's come home--"

The PET SET

"It's not like the boss to be late--"

The PET SET

"Someday, would you mind feeding _me_ first?"

The PET SET

"I can't leave you--they'd be lost without me."

The PET SET

Doug & Jean   © D&J Borgstedt   1-16

"C'mon, TRY it baby--you'll like it!"

The PET SET

"I don't care if they ARE clean, intelligent and affectionate--the answer is NO!"

The PET SET

"What I like is--you don't have to walk 'em, train 'em, brush 'em, or listen to them."

The PET SET

"The first time can be a very shattering experience."

The PET SET

"I remember when you used to flutter around like that to get my attention."

The PET SET

"Let me know if there are any false moves I shouldn't make--"

The PET SET

"If they can't sleep on the bed with me,
I'm sleepin' on the floor with them!"

The PET SET

"Hold it, folks--!"

The PET SET

"I figure a dog's good protection nowadays."

The PET SET

"I can't understand it--the boys just don't seem interested in our Mary."

The PET SET

"I wonder if there's a Dr. Spock for puppies!"

The PET SET

4-14 © D & J Borgstedt

"Let's give up naming them and just number them."

The PET SET

"Residents of Elm Street expecting
mail -- come and get it!"

The PET SET

"Do you mind sitting over here, Reverend?
That's HER chair."

The PET SET

"Sure I'm his owner. Why?"

The PET SET

"The dog bones are meatier--THAT'S why I shop here."

The PET SET

© D&J Borgstedt

"So THAT'S where my hamster was."

The **PET SET**

"It's 4th down and one to go right here,
in case you haven't noticed."

The PET SET

"It's her turn to sleep on <u>my</u> bed!"

The PET SET

"I hope to get some tips on
zero population growth."

The PET SET

"Now the next two reels show them
at four to six months."

The PET SET

"Everybody comfy back there?"

The PET SET

"I put everybody to sleep but him!"

The PET SET

"YOU go in--you made the reservations."

The PET SET

"I didn't begin to worry, till he started chirping in his sleep."